3 Give the number (e.g. 2nd, 3rd) of each of these harmonic intervals, as shown in the answer. The key is B♭ major.

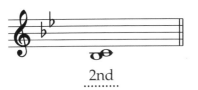 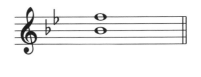 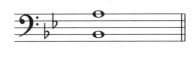

2nd
....

....

....

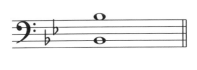 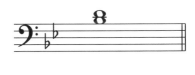 

....

....

....

4 Rewrite this melody *without* using a key signature. Remember to include sharp, flat or natural signs where they are needed. The key is E♭ major and the first bar is given.

J. S. Bach

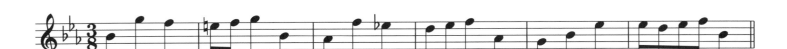

5 Add the correct clef and any necessary sharp or flat signs to make each of the scales named below. Do *not* use key signatures.

A major

D minor

Which form of the minor scale have you used? ....

6 Name the keys of these tonic triads.

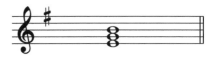

....

....

....

....

....

7 (a) Rewrite these bass clef notes in the treble clef, keeping the pitch the same. The first answer is given.

(b) In which major key are all these notes found? ....

4

8 Look at this melody by Mozart and then answer the questions below.

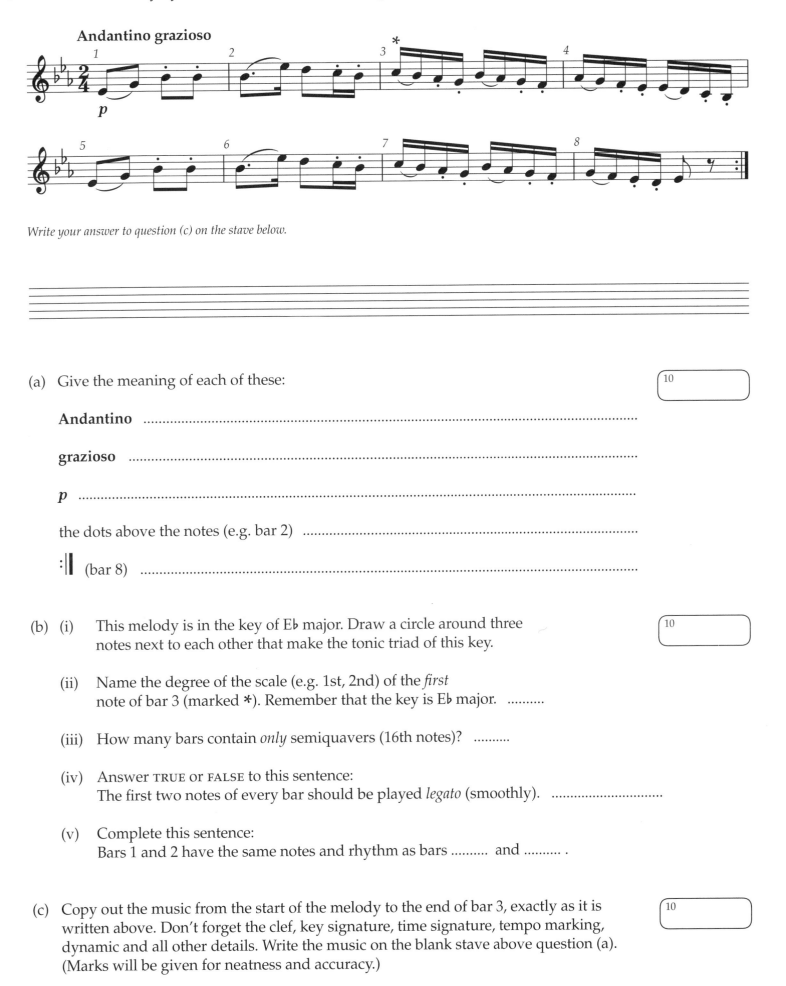

Write your answer to question (c) on the stave below.

(a) Give the meaning of each of these:

Andantino ....

grazioso ....

p ....

the dots above the notes (e.g. bar 2) ....

:|| (bar 8) ....

[10]

(b) (i) This melody is in the key of E♭ major. Draw a circle around three notes next to each other that make the tonic triad of this key.

[10]

(ii) Name the degree of the scale (e.g. 1st, 2nd) of the *first* note of bar 3 (marked ✶). Remember that the key is E♭ major. ....

(iii) How many bars contain *only* semiquavers (16th notes)? ....

(iv) Answer TRUE or FALSE to this sentence:
The first two notes of every bar should be played *legato* (smoothly). ....

(v) Complete this sentence:
Bars 1 and 2 have the same notes and rhythm as bars .... and ....

(c) Copy out the music from the start of the melody to the end of bar 3, exactly as it is written above. Don't forget the clef, key signature, time signature, tempo marking, dynamic and all other details. Write the music on the blank stave above question (a). (Marks will be given for neatness and accuracy.)

[10]

Theory Paper Grade 2   2009   B

Duration 1¹/₂ hours

TOTAL MARKS
100

Candidates should answer ALL questions.
Write your answers on this paper – no others will be accepted.
Answers must be written clearly and neatly – otherwise marks may be lost.

1   Add the missing bar-lines to these two melodies. The first bar-line is given in each.

10

Legrenzi

Albinoni

2   Write a four-bar rhythm using the given opening.

10

3 Add the correct clef to make each of these named notes, as shown in the first answer. [10]

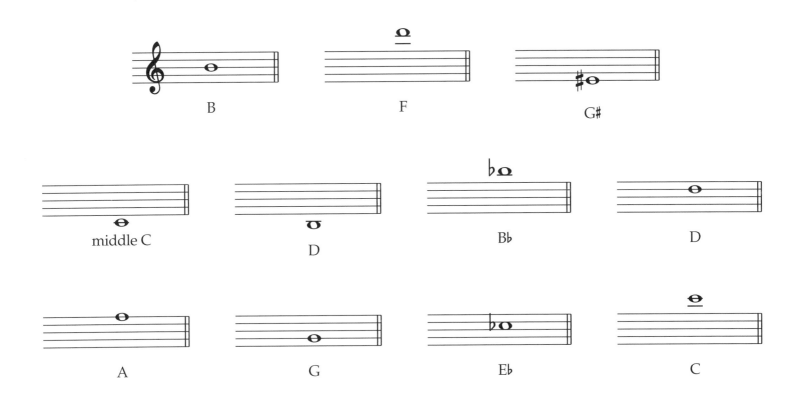

4 Rewrite this melody using the correct key signature. Leave out any unnecessary accidentals, but remember to include any that are needed. The key is A major and the first three notes are given. [10]

5 Name each key as shown by its key signature. The first answer is given.

10

......E..... minor

.... major

.... minor

.... major

.... major

.... minor

6 Write as semibreves (whole notes) the scales named below.

10

D major, descending, with key signature.

A minor, ascending, without key signature but adding any necessary sharp or flat signs.

Which form of the minor scale have you used? ....

7 (a) Name the degree of the scale (e.g. 2nd, 3rd) of each of the notes marked *, as shown in the first answer. The key is E♭ major.

10

Wagner

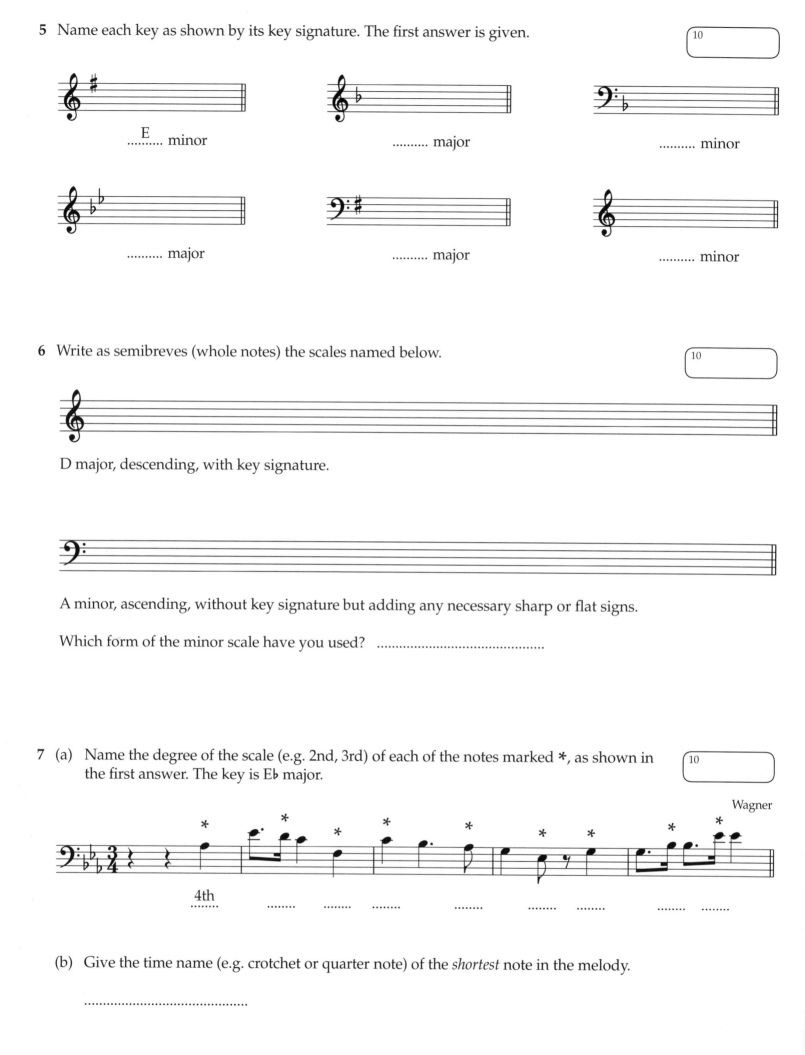

4th
....

....
....
....

....

....
....

....
....

(b) Give the time name (e.g. crotchet or quarter note) of the *shortest* note in the melody.

....

8

8 Look at this melody by Haydn and then answer the questions below.

Write your answer to question (c) on the stave below.

(a) Give the meaning of each of these: 10

Presto   ....

the **8** in $\frac{3}{8}$ ....

f   ....

⌢ (e.g. bar 1)   ....

the dots below the notes (e.g. bar 2)   ....

(b) (i)   This melody is in the key of C major. Draw a circle   10
around a note that is the 7th degree of the scale.

(ii)   Answer TRUE or FALSE to this sentence: Bars 1 and 6 are the only
two bars that contain all three notes of the tonic triad of C major.   ....

(iii)   How many times does the rhythm occur?   ....

(iv)   How many bars contain *only* quavers (eighth notes)?   ....

(v)   Give the letter name of the *highest* note in the melody.   ....

(c) Copy out the music from the start of the melody to the end of bar 6, exactly as it is   10
written above. Don't forget the clef, time signature, tempo marking, dynamic and all
other details. Write the music on the blank stave above question (a).
(Marks will be given for neatness and accuracy.)

Theory Paper Grade 2   2009   C

Duration 1 ¹/₂ hours

TOTAL MARKS
100

Candidates should answer ALL questions.
Write your answers on this paper – no others will be accepted.
Answers must be written clearly and neatly – otherwise marks may be lost.

1   Add the missing bar-lines to these two melodies. The first bar-line is given in each.

10

Paisiello

J. S. Bach

2   Write a four-bar rhythm using the given opening.

10

3   Rewrite this melody in the bass clef, keeping the pitch the same.
    The first two notes are given.

10

Bruckner

4 Add the correct clef and any necessary sharp or flat signs to make each of the scales named below. Do *not* use key signatures.

Bb major

A minor

Which form of the minor scale have you used? ....

5 Add the correct rest(s) at the places marked * in these two melodies to make each bar complete.

11

6 Write the tonic triads named below. Do *not* use key signatures, but remember to add any necessary sharp or flat signs.

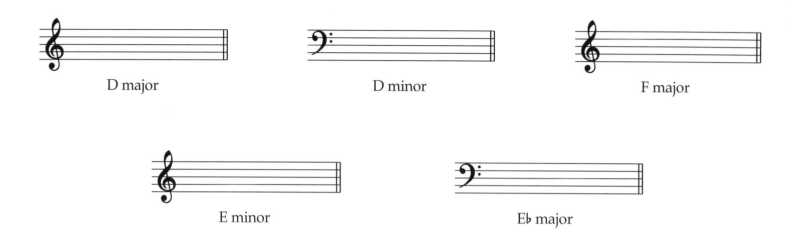

7 (a) Name the degree of the scale (e.g. 2nd, 3rd) of each of the notes marked *, as shown in the first answer. The key is A major.

(b) Give the time name (e.g. crotchet or quarter note) of the rest in the first bar. ....

8 Look at this folksong melody and then answer the questions below.

Write your answer to question (c) on the stave below.

(a) Give the meaning of each of these: [10]

Moderato ....

sostenuto ....

⌣ (e.g. bar 1) ....

cresc. (e.g. bar 7) ....

mf (bar 8) ....

(b) (i) This melody is in the key of E minor. Give the number of
a bar that contains all three notes of the tonic triad of this key. Bar .... [10]

(ii) Complete this sentence:
Bar 1 has the same notes and rhythm as bar ....

(iii) Give the letter name of the last note in bar 3 (marked *). ....

(iv) How many bars contain a triplet? ....

(v) In which bar is the performer told to pause or hold on to the note? Bar ....

(c) Copy out the music from the start of bar 6 to the end of the melody, exactly as it is
written above. Don't forget the clef, key signature, dynamics and all other details.
Write the music on the blank stave above question (a).
(Marks will be given for neatness and accuracy.) [10]

Theory Paper Grade 2   2009   S

Duration 1 $^{1}/_{2}$ hours

Candidates should answer ALL questions.
Write your answers on this paper – no others will be accepted.
Answers must be written clearly and neatly – otherwise marks may be lost.

1   Add the missing bar-lines to these two melodies. The first bar-line is given in each.

J. S. Bach

D. Scarlatti

2   Write a four-bar rhythm using the given opening.

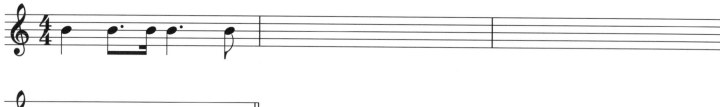

3   (a)   Give the letter name of each of the notes marked **∗**, including the sharp or flat sign where necessary. The first answer is given.

Beethoven

(b)   How many quavers (eighth notes) are the tied notes in the last two bars worth in total?   ....

4 Rewrite this melody in the treble clef, keeping the pitch the same. The first note is given.

Dvořák

5 *After* each note write a higher note to form the named *melodic* interval, as shown in the first answer. The key is E♭ major.

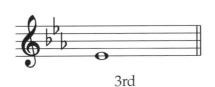

6th

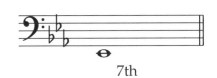

2nd

7th

4th

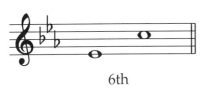

3rd

5th

6 Add the correct rest(s) at the places marked * in this melody to make each bar complete.

Handel

7 Rewrite the following melody, grouping (beaming) the notes correctly.

Albinoni

8 Look at this melody by J. C. F. Bach and then answer the questions below.

Write your answer to question (c) on the stave below.

(a) Give the meaning of each of these: 10

Allegretto ....

the **2 in ²⁄₄** ....

𝑓 ....

the dots above the notes (e.g. bar 3) ....

⌒ (bar 8) ....

(b) (i)   This melody is in the key of B♭ major. Give the number of a   10
            bar that contains all the notes of the tonic triad of this key. Bar ....

     (ii) Draw a circle around two notes next to each other that are an 8ve/8th apart.

     (iii) Complete this sentence:
            Bar 1 has the same notes and rhythm as bar ....

     (iv) Give the letter name of the first note in bar 4 (marked *). ....

     (v)   Answer TRUE or FALSE to this sentence:
            This melody uses all the degrees of the scale (1st, 2nd etc.) of B♭ major. ....

(c) Copy out the music from the start of bar 5 to the end of the melody, exactly as it is   10
     written above. Don't forget the clef, key signature and all other details.
     Write the music on the blank stave above question (a).
     (Marks will be given for neatness and accuracy.)

ABRSM
24 Portland Place
London W1B 1LU
United Kingdom

www.abrsm.org

*Theory of Music Exams Model Answers,
2009, Grades 1 to 8 are available now
from your usual retailer.*

Published by ABRSM (Publishing) Ltd,
a wholly owned subsidiary of ABRSM

Printed in England by Halstan & Co. Ltd,
Amersham, Bucks 10/09

ISBN 978-1-84849-128-1